# *Mary* QUEEN OF *SCOTS*

CORBIE

Text by David Ross
Illustrated by Jane Taylor, Genus Art

© 1998 Waverley Books Ltd
Reprinted 1999, 2002

Published by Waverley Books Ltd,
New Lanark, Scotland

ISBN 1 902407 01 6

Printed and bound in Slovenia

# THE STORY OF
# MARY
## Queen of Scots

**M**y name is Mary Seton. I am an old woman now, but once I was a young girl. The story I am going to tell you starts when I was young. It is not about me but about another girl called Mary. Her father was James the Fifth, the king of Scotland. She was the only child of James and his queen.

Mary was born in the royal palace at Linlithgow, near Edinburgh, but her father died when she was only a few days old. She was only a tiny baby, but she was also the queen of Scotland.

When she was still only nine months old, she was crowned. Some of the great lords of Scotland were there. The crown was held above her head by the Earl of Arran. The baby's head was far too small for the crown to fit, and the crown was far too heavy. The Earl of Lennox held the sceptre for her, and the sword of state was carried by the Earl of Argyll.

Scotland at that time was a rough and dangerous country. Without a king to keep them in order, the lords and earls would fight among themselves. One of them, the Earl of Arran, was made governor of Scotland, to look after the country until Mary grew up. But the other lords did not pay much attention to him. They were always

ready to seek help from the king of England, who at this time was the famous Henry the Eighth. The kings of England had always been interested in Scotland, in the same way that a cat is interested in a mouse. Henry had a plan for the little Queen Mary. When she grew older, she should marry his young son, Prince Edward, who at that time was five years old. One day Edward would be king of England and then England and Scotland would become one country.

Some people in Scotland did not like Henry's plan. One of these was the baby queen's mother, also called Queen Mary. We will call her the Queen Mother. There are a lot of Marys in this story! You will meet more of us soon.

This Mary had come from France to marry King James of Scotland. She had a large family in France, where they were very important people. France and Scotland had always been friendly to each other while France and England had always fought. The Queen Mother knew that Scotland could not be friends with both England and France. She wanted to carry on being friends with France. King Henry actually wanted the baby to be sent to London and brought up in his palace, and the Queen Mother did not want to lose her child. Although the baby was still so young, other people too had plans for whom Mary should marry. The Earl of Arran thought she should marry his young son.

What both these men thought was this – even though Mary was the rightful queen of Scotland, her husband would surely be the actual ruler and perhaps even become the king. Scotland had never before been ruled by a woman.

Mary was brought up in the strong castle of Stirling, built on a steep rock. It was a fortress, but inside its walls was a royal palace, built by her father and grandfather. Even there she was not safe. King Henry of England sent his armies into Scotland. The first time, they set the whole town of Edinburgh on fire and burned down the royal palace there. The second time, a Scottish army was waiting and defeated them. But they came back again and destroyed many towns and burned the newly harvested corn. To the people of Scotland this seemed a very strange way of asking for their

little queen to marry Henry's son! Even after Henry died, the English still sent armies into Scotland, and there was another battle at Pinkie Cleugh in which the Scottish army was badly defeated.

The child knew little of these events. She was still very young. In the palace at Stirling she had her nurse and her toys. Above all, she had her mother. The Queen Mother dearly loved her only daughter and spent as much time with her as she could. When sometimes they had to move suddenly, it was an adventure for the little girl. Once they hurried to Dunkeld and stayed in the bishop's house by the cathedral. Once she was taken to a beautiful island, Inchmahome, on the Lake of Menteith. She always loved the open air. From the high battlements of Stirling Castle, her nurse could lift her up to see the hills of the Highlands, only a few miles away. At Dunkeld and Inchmahome, she was among those hills.

After the battle of Pinkie, the English army did not go back but stayed in Scotland. The Scots now asked France for help to drive the English out. It was decided that the little queen should be sent to France for her own safety in case the English should capture her.

Then something awful happened. The little queen suddenly became very ill. Lying in her bed, hot and feverish, she could not speak. Some people thought she was going to die. What would happen if she did die? At least two of the Scottish nobles would claim the throne. There would certainly be a war. Luckily she got better again quite quickly.

The Queen Mother had now found a suitable husband for her daughter. This was Francis, the young son of the king of France. He was younger than Mary. The Queen Mother was not going to go to France with Mary. She was determined to stay on in Scotland to look after the kingdom for her daughter until Mary grew up and could rule by herself. The Queen Mother knew that if she went away, Mary might never be able to claim her kingdom. Either one of the Scottish lords would try to make himself king or else the English would take it over.

This is where I, Mary Seton, come into the story. My father was Lord Seton, a great Scottish nobleman. Four little girls were chosen to go to France as companions of the queen. We were all called Mary, which in French is Marie, and we were the four Maries. There was me, and also Mary

Fleming, Mary Beaton and Mary Livingston. I was the one to serve the queen longest.

I remember how sad we felt at leaving Scotland. The Queen Mother wept as she hugged her child, who was still only five years old. But for us

children it was also a great adventure. The voyage to France was very stormy. I was seasick. I lay down in a smelly little bunk, feeling terrible. But the queen was not sick at all, and I remember how she unmercifully teased me and the other Maries about how green we looked.

What a welcome was waiting for us in France! It was as if we had been rescued from fire-breathing dragons. We travelled in state through the country. Everything seemed bigger and grander than in

Scotland. For a time we went by boat down a huge river, with musicians playing aboard, to the castle where the royal family of France lived. From being an only child, with only grown-up people for company, the queen was now in the nursery rooms with the prince and princess of France. She still had her Scottish nurse, Janet Sinclair, but sadly for us, I and the other little Maries were not allowed to stay with her at this time. We were sent to be looked after by nuns. Her best friend at this time was the little Princess Elisabeth of France. It was here too that she met Francis, who would one day be king of France and she would be his queen. He was a strange, moody, thin little boy with a runny nose, but he loved Mary even as a child. She was the opposite of him – as pretty as a flower, quick to laugh, quick to cry and as full of life and energy as a spring lamb.

These were happy years for the young Mary Queen of Scots. She and the French royal children played games; they learned to ride; they had wardrobes full of beautiful dresses. There were lessons, too, but there was plenty of time for fun and games. Everyone was kind to them. And, because she was a queen, Mary always went first when they appeared before King Henry of France,

Francis's father. He was very fond of her and said that she was the most perfect child he had ever seen.

After long years, I saw her again when she and Francis were married. She was fifteen years old and he was only fourteen. I thought she might have forgotten little Mary Seton, but she ran to embrace me just as when we had been childhood friends. I was one of the crowd in the great cathedral of Paris, Notre Dame, to see them wed. In the brilliant gathering, she stood out like a bright flower.

She was wearing a magnificent pure white robe with a long train carried by two young girls. Already taller than her young husband, she wore a golden crown on her head and a great necklace of diamonds round her neck. Even among the queens and duchesses who were there, her youth, her beauty and her pride stood out. This was the high point of her life. She was queen of Scots and was married to the future king of France. She also knew, and so did everyone else, that she had a strong claim to be the queen of England. It was a breathtaking idea that this teenage girl might unite three ancient kingdoms.

But it was not to be. Sooner than she supposed, Mary indeed became queen of France, when her father-in-law, King Henry, died of an injury he received while jousting in a tournament. Her little, sniffling, loving Francis became king of the mighty realm of France, but in less than two years he was dead of an ear infection and Mary became a widow. She was only eighteen.

France had a new king. But she still was a queen in her own right, with a kingdom she had not seen since she was five years old. Mary returned to Scotland, and I, with the other three Maries, went with her. She chose me to be her lady-in-waiting.

She loved beautiful things and so did I, and I had learned how to dress her long, fair hair in the way that she liked and to help choose her clothes. I soothed her when she was fretful. It was not easy for her, being queen. There were happy days, when she was out in the countryside. She always loved the open air, and she rode like a real dare-devil. I was often afraid that she would fall and hurt herself. Sometimes she dressed as a boy so that people would not recognise her and then she could gallop as fast as she liked. Sometimes, too, she dressed not as a queen but as any other woman of Edinburgh and slipped out through the gates of her palace to walk in the streets, free for a short time of the burden of royalty.

Scotland was a difficult country to rule. The lords were all jealous of each other. They would not work together to help the queen and the country. Queen Mary had been brought up in the old Catholic religion, but many people in Scotland now followed the new Protestant religion. Led by Master John Knox, they were not willing to let their queen worship the same God in a different way. There were many arguments and disputes over this, and the queen and I often shed tears.

Since now she had no husband, many different men wanted to marry her. In the end she married the handsome young Henry Stuart, Lord Darnley. They had a child, Prince James, which made everyone rejoice. I remember seeing the hundreds of bonfires lit in Edinburgh to celebrate the birth of a child who would be the next king of Scotland. But the marriage ended in disaster. Darnley wanted not just to be the queen's husband but to be king. He was vain, greedy, lazy and ill-natured.

The queen soon discovered this and did not allow Darnley to help her rule the country. He was jealous of her secretary, David Riccio, who knew her secrets. One dreadful evening, as she sat with Riccio in her palace of Holyrood in Edinburgh, Darnley and a gang of his friends burst in, dragged David Riccio out of the room and killed him with their daggers. More terrible things followed. Darnley himself was murdered. He was recovering from smallpox in a house called Kirk o' Field, which was blown up by gunpowder. He was found lying dead in the garden. This was the work of the Earl of Bothwell and his friends, but many people murmured that Queen Mary herself knew about it and perhaps had even ordered it to happen. And the people of Scotland, who had at first loved their beautiful young queen, began to speak against her.

Even worse was to come. The Earl of Bothwell said he was the queen's defender. Other great lords said he was trying to make himself the ruler of Scotland. My poor queen was caught in the rivalry of these harsh men. She did not know what to do. On an evil day, only a few months after Darnley's murder, she married the Earl of Bothwell, making him the Duke of Orkney. The other lords raised an army, and after only five weeks, Bothwell ran away and the queen was imprisoned in the island castle of Loch Leven.

For more than a year she was locked up in that grim old castle – she who loved to ride at speed out on the hills and moors. I returned to our own house, Seton Palace. The Earl of Moray was made regent of the kingdom, and he forced Mary to sign a paper to say that she was no longer queen. Her baby son, James, was proclaimed as king. Scotland was now ruled by the Earl of Moray and his friends.

But the Queen still had some true friends. I knew that my father, Lord Seton, was trying to have her set free, but it was she herself who arranged her escape from Loch Leven.

Her jailer was the stern Sir William Douglas, but two members of his own family were so charmed by her that they became her loyal friends and secret helpers. George Douglas met my father and arranged for him to be close to the shore of Loch Leven on a certain day with a strong party of his men. On that day, young Willy Douglas stole the keys of the castle from under the very nose of Sir William and unlocked the main gate. The queen, dressed like a country woman, slipped out through the gate. Willy locked it again and led her down to where a boat was waiting. Soon they were on the mainland. To the queen's delight, people cheered her as she rode through the country with my father and his men. Soon, she thought, she would be back in her palace and back on the throne.

Alas, poor queen! Once again the lords of Scotland were her undoing. The Earl of Moray rallied his supporters and raised an army. The queen's supporters had a larger army, but when the two met at the village of Langside near Glasgow, the queen's chief general, the Earl of

Argyll, did not order his men to attack. It is said that he was in league with the other side. The queen's army was totally defeated. Like a true warrior queen, she had tried to ride into the battle

herself to urge her men forward. Instead of riding in triumph to Edinburgh, she had to flee into the south in a long, exhausting ride. She had made the fateful decision to leave Scotland and go to England to ask for the help of her royal cousin, Queen Elizabeth.

Queen Elizabeth had no help to offer. She believed Queen Mary was a dangerous rival whose real aim was to become queen of England. She kept the Queen of Scots a prisoner for nearly twenty years while Mary's young son, James, grew up and became the ruler of Scotland. She never saw him again, and he made no effort to have her set free. Through it all, the Setons supported her. My father, Lord Seton, whose guest she had often been in our great house, was taken prisoner in her last battle against the rebel lords. Through many long years of her captivity in England, I was with her, the last of her four Maries. We sewed tapestries, we sang, read poems to each other, we talked about happier days long ago and prayed for happier days to come. And still I helped her with her dresses and her ornaments of gold. But at last I became ill. With the queen's permission, I retired, not to Scotland with its unhappy memories, but to France. From there I used to send her little gifts and loving messages. And it was there I heard the news, one grim day early in the year of 1587, that under the orders of Elizabeth of England, my queen had been put to death.

# SOME DATES IN THE LIFE OF MARY QUEEN OF SCOTS

- Born 8th December 1542

- Became queen of Scotland on 14th December 1542

- Sent to France in August 1548

- Married to the Dauphin Francis on 24th April 1558

- Became queen of France on 10th July 1559

- Widowed on 20th November 1560

- Returned to Scotland on 19th August 1561

- Married to Lord Darnley on 29th July 1565

- Murder of David Riccio on 9th March 1566

- Murder of Lord Darnley on 9th February 1567

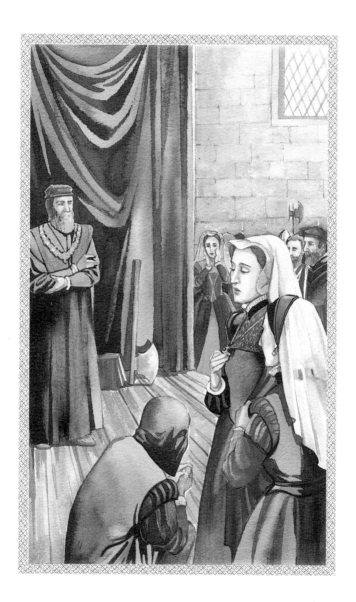

- Married to Earl of Bothwell on 15th May 1567

- Imprisoned in Loch Leven Castle, June 1567

- Escape from Loch Leven on 2nd May 1568

- Battle of Langside on 13th May 1568

- Flight to England, May 1568

- Execution at Fotheringay Castle on 8th February 1587